JAZZ PIANO PLUS

John Kember

14 original jazz pieces for piano with optional teacher part
14 Originalkompositionen für Klavier mit zweitem Klavierpart nach Belieben
14 morceaux de jazz originaux avec, en option, une partie pour le professeur

CONTENTS

Note on 'swing' rhythm
In this book, pieces to be played with a 'swing' feel are indicated:
In all other cases, quavers/eighth notes should be played straight.

© 2005 by Faber Music Ltd
First published in 2005 by Faber Music Ltd
3 Queen Square London WC1N 3AU
Cover illustration by Vikki Liogier
Music processed by Christopher Hinkins
Printed in England by Caligraving Ltd
All rights reserved

ISBN 0-571-52373-0

To buy Faber Music publications or to find out about the full range of titles available
please contact your local music retailer or Faber Music sales enquiries:

Faber Music Limited, Burnt Mill, Elizabeth Way, Harlow, CM20 2HX England
Tel: +44 (0)1279 82 89 82   Fax: +44 (0)1279 82 89 83
sales@fabermusic.com   fabermusic.com

1. SATURDAY NIGHT

2. RHYTHMIC RUMBA

3. STRAIGHT TALKING

4. BALLAD

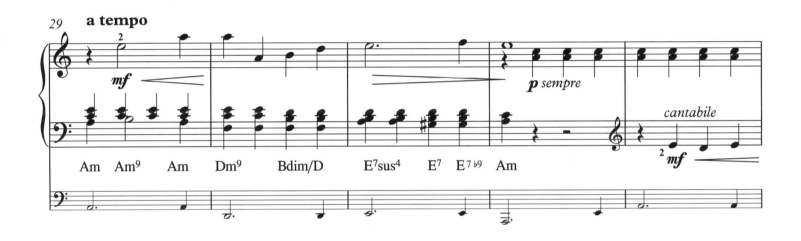

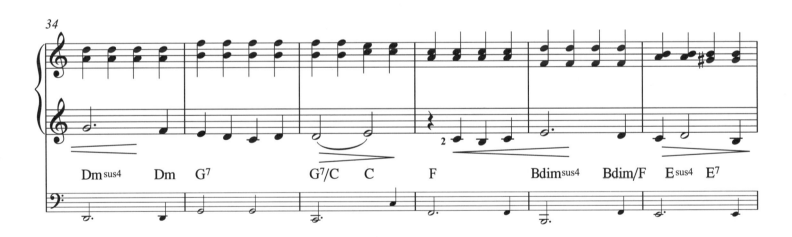

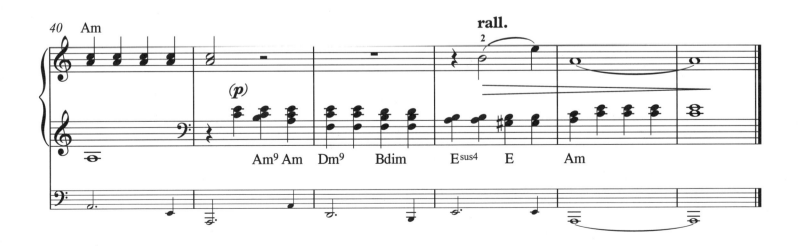

5. HAVING A STOMP

6. ROOTLESS CHORDS

In 'rootless' chords the root is either implied, or played in an additional bass line. In 2-note chords, the 7th is played and the tonality provided by the 3rd. 3- and 4-note chords enable notes in addition to the 3rd and 7th to be included. These are mainly the 9th and 6th.

Basic rootless chord voicings

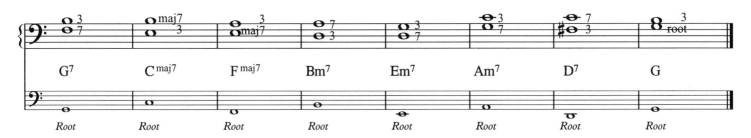

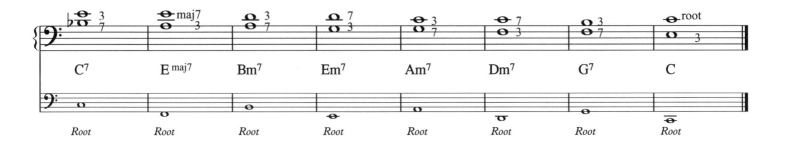

3-note voicings

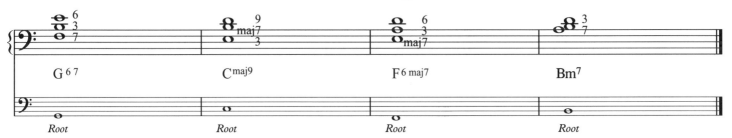

3- and 4-note voicings

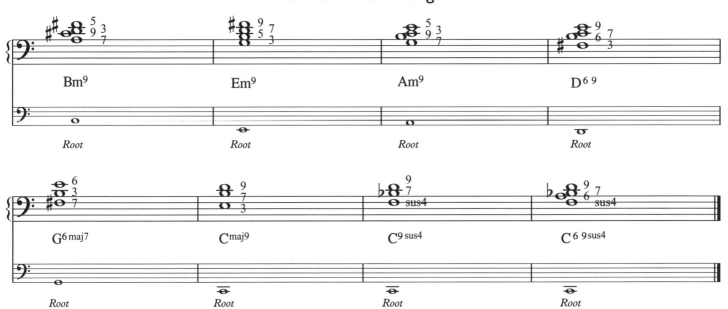

7. CHILLIN' OUT

8. LUCY'S BLUES

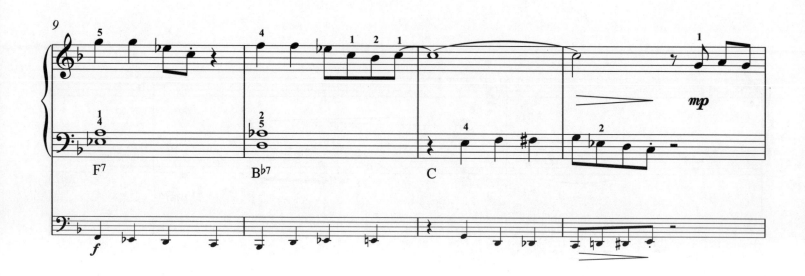

9. PAST MIDNIGHT

* on D.S., make changes to melody

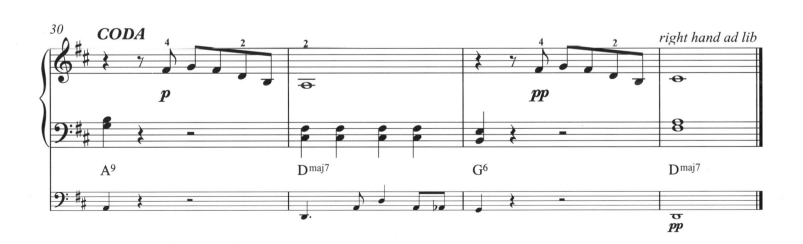

10. LEFT HAND COMPING
(WITH ADDED BASS LINE)

Swing feel
on the first beat

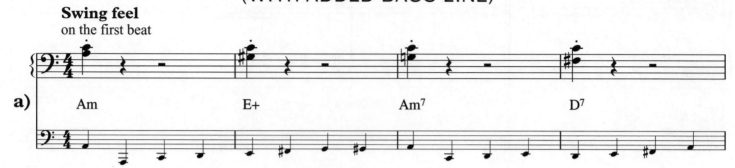

a) Am   E+   Am⁷   D⁷

Dm⁷   G⁷   C maj7   F maj7

with fuller chords

b) Am   E+   Am⁷   D⁹

Dm⁹   G⁷   C maj7   F maj7

first beat and anticipated 4th beat

c) Am   E+   Am⁷   D⁹

2nd beat and anticipated
4th and 1st beats

d)

1st beat quavers/eighth notes
anticipated 4th and 1st beats

e)

11. TAKE IT AWAY

12. OUT FOR THE COUNT

* on D.S., make changes to melody

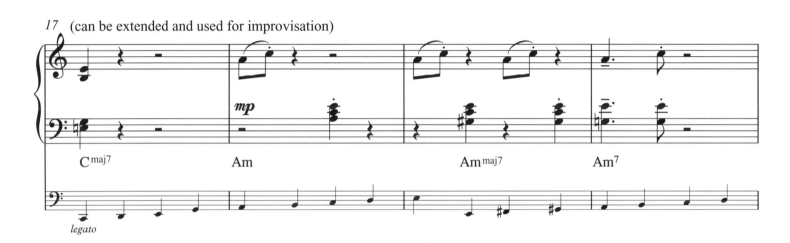

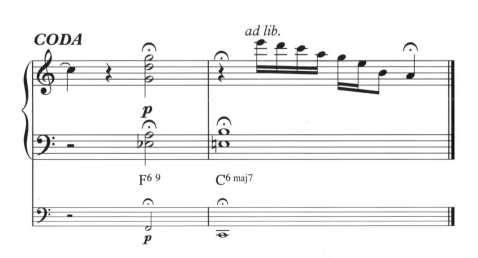

13. OUT AND ABOUT

14. WALK THAT BASS!